The
STairWay
To Heaven

Vivian and Max Discover
the Way to Heaven

Victoria M. Howard

Trilogy Christian Publishers
A Wholly Owned Subsidary of Trinity Broadcasting Network
2442 Michelle Drive
Tustin, CA 92780

Cover design by: Cornerstone Creative Solutions

For information, address Trilogy Christian Publishing
Rights Department, 2442 Michelle Drive, Tustin, Ca 92780.
Trilogy Christian Publishing/ TBN and colophon are trademarks of Trinity Broadcasting Network.

For information about special discounts for bulk purchases, please contact Trilogy Christian Publishing.

Manufactured in the United States of America

10 9 8 7 6 5 4 3 2 1

Library of Congress Cataloging-in-Publication Data is available.

ISBN 978-1-68556-252-6 (Print Book)
ISBN 978-1-68556-253-3 (ebook)

For my granddaughter, Vivian Grace

Contents

Preface

Is heaven real, and if it is, who can go there, and how do we get there?

Some questions that have been asked since the beginning of time include: *What happens to us after we die? Will we see our loved ones again? What happens to our pets when they die—is there a special place in heaven for them?*

We can only imagine what heaven looks like.

In many movies, heaven is portrayed as having endless fields of colorful flowers, blue sky with white puffy clouds, beautiful horses roaming the landscape, and angels hovering around singing beautiful songs.

Yes, we all have questions about what heaven will be like, but no one has ever come back from the dead to give us the answers—except for one Person: our Lord and Savior, Jesus Christ.

I'm happy to tell you that heaven is, indeed, a real place.

How do I know this?

The Bible tells us that heaven is God's throne (Isaiah 66:1; Acts 7:48–49; Matthew 5:34–35), and in 2 Corinthians 12:1–4, the apostle Paul referred to heaven, or "paradise," as a heavenly realm, or the "third heaven."

The third heaven is separate from the first heaven (which includes the skies above us that cover the earth) and the second heaven (which is where the stars, moon, and sun reside—the expanse of outer space).

The third heaven cannot be seen, but it's the place where God, Jesus Christ, and all those who died believing in Jesus live. Heaven is where the people of God will all go and live one day.

In *The Stairway to Heaven*, Max, the Bolognese dog, along with his owner, a five-year-old girl named Vivian (Vivi) Grace sets out on a journey to discover Paradise—heaven.

Along the way, they encounter different situations and learn important lessons, allowing them to climb one step closer toward heaven's gate.

In the broken world in which we live today, it's important to choose what our children are exposed to and reveal to them things that are beautiful, that are noble, and that highlight good character.

Reading to your children is one of the best gifts you can give them, as you share positive stories that teach them about Jesus Christ and what He did for them. It is our duty as parents and disciples of God.

Max and Vivian will teach the truths of Scripture to your child in a fun and easy way, including the Ten Commandments, the story of Adam and Eve, Jesus' miracles, how Jesus saved us by dying on the cross, and how to live our lives so that we can one day live in that Paradise in the sky—heaven.

Introduction

Children are the purest, most innocent creatures God created. In the Bible—from the beginning to the end of God's Word—God speaks about the importance and worth of children. Children have great significance in God's plan, and numerous Bible verses speak of children being a blessing.

Childhood should be silly, fun, and free, but being a child today is not easy, for they live in the shadow of adults—a much different species than themselves.

Children are often misunderstood, and they can be easily crushed by adults who don't have enough time to listen to them. This is especially true today, when in many cases, both parents must work to provide for the family.

As a child grows, change occurs, and change can trigger fear, doubt, and confusion. Two of the most common questions children ask are, *What happens when we die?* and *Where do we go when we die?*

Death is often a very scary thing to a small child. It's alarming for many adults, too, if they are not saved—for it's only through Jesus Christ's salvation that we can go to heaven.

Our duty as parents is to help ease our children's tension and anxiety and assure them that during difficult times, they don't have to be afraid, for they are never alone—Jesus Christ is always with them.

The Stairway to Heaven is written so that children can understand the concept of heaven, for they will easily identify with the main characters, Max, the Bolognese dog, and Vivian Grace, as they set out on a journey to answer these mystifying questions.

Along the way, they discover God, who is their mentor. He is by their side as they encounter uncertain and fearful situations. These stories will help build your child's relationship with God by introducing them to scripturally based characteristics of who He is—a good and loving God who is always watching over us.

This book was written for children of all ages—for we are all children at heart, are we not?

God is omnipotent and omniscient, and He has prepared a place for His children. I hope you enjoy reading this book with your child, as you help answer their questions and assure them of what's waiting for them in heaven.

8

*In My Father's house are many dwelling
places; if it were not so, I would have told
you; for I go to prepare a place for you.*
                    —John 14:2 NASB1995

1

Is Heaven Real?

It was another beautiful summer day in Florida.

"Come on, Max. Let's go to the dog park and enjoy this beautiful day that God has given us," the girl said to her dog.

"Okay, Vivi. I'd like that," said Max.

After they arrived at the park, it started to rain, but the showers only lasted a few minutes before a beautiful double rainbow appeared in the sky.

The colors of the rainbow were magnificent! Shades of red, yellow, green, blue, and violet filled the sky.

"Wow! It is so beautiful," Max said, shaking the raindrops from his fur.

"This is another one of God's many miracles and gifts to us. Do you think a rainbow is a sign from God trying to tell us something?" asked Vivi.

After some thought, Max answered, "Well, the Bible seems to say so."

"What do you mean?" Vivi looked confused.

"The Book of Revelation tells us that an angel came down from heaven, wrapped in a cloud with a rainbow over his head. And in Genesis, God told Noah that the rainbow is a sign of His covenant with all the creatures on the earth. And after the flood, God used the rainbow as a sign of His promise never to destroy the earth again by water," Max explained. "So, yes, a rainbow can be a sign from God to show people certain things."

"Wow! Can we touch a rainbow?" Vivi asked.

"No, silly girl. Rainbows are in heaven." Max laughed.

"Well, then, let's go to heaven so we can touch the rainbows," Vivi said.

"No, Vivi, you can't go to heaven today. People and animals only go to heaven when they die," answered Max.

"*DIE!* I don't want to die! And how do we even know heaven is real? When I ask my mom, she says it is, because the Bible tells us that heaven is where God and the angels live."

Vivi tilted her head. "And how do we get there? Is there a street that takes us to heaven?" Vivi asked Max.

"No, there is no street to get there, but there *is* a stairway to heaven."

After thinking about it, Vivi jumped up and down.

"A stairway to heaven! Well, then, let's go and find it."

As they entered a field of high, overgrown weeds at the far end of the park, a stairway appeared before them.

It was simply beautiful! The steps were made of gold that started at their feet and reached high into the sky.

At the very top of the stairway, a brilliant light emanated from the puffy clouds.

As Max and Vivi stepped on the bottom step, they heard a man's voice.

"Welcome, My children. You cannot come up the steps until you first learn some very important lessons. Listen to Me, and I will guide you," He said.

"Who is that?" Vivi asked Max.

"That is our heavenly Father, God. We had better do as He says."

14

*"Then I saw another mighty angel coming
down from heaven, wrapped in a cloud, with
a rainbow over his head, and his face was like
the sun, and his legs like pillars of fire."*
—Revelation 10:1 ESV

2

Jesus is the Son of God

Vivi's voice quivered as she asked, "Father, what is the first lesson we must learn?"

Although the girl and dog couldn't see anyone, they heard a comforting voice come down from the sky.

"The first lesson in the Basics of Salvation you must learn is that Jesus is the Son of God," the voice boomed.

A puzzled look crossed Vivi's face.

"How can Jesus be the Son of God?" she asked. "I thought Jesus *was* God!"

The heavenly Father smiled and said, "In the beginning, God created the world, and He made human beings in His own image. Although Jesus was once a child like you are, Vivi, He was also the one and only Son of God—the Creator of everything. I have loved you so much that I gave you the most wonderful gift of all—My Son. Anyone who believes in Him will not die but have everlasting life."

The voice continued, "Before the earth, sun, moon, or stars were created, My Son, Jesus, was here with Me, His Father. But there was a time when Jesus became a man. He lived on the earth for thirty-three years. He came to save the world and to do My will, the will of His Father.

"Jesus was born in the image of a man so that He could save sinners and give them eternal life. I want everyone to know who My Son, Jesus, is and what He has done for them."

Max spoke up. "Well, that's easy! I believe that Jesus is the Son of God, and so does Vivi. Don't you, Vivi?"

Vivi smiled. "Of course I believe. Doesn't everybody?" She hesitated.

God quietly answered, "No, honey. Unfortunately, many people don't believe in Me. Some people don't believe in Me because they want to run their own lives. They don't want anyone—especially Me—to interfere with the way they want to live. They believe they know more than I do. That's a *big* mistake!

"But to live without Me is to live without hope. Instead of understanding that I put them on earth for a purpose, they live their lives without any meaning. It's very sad."

Vivi knew someone in that situation. "My friend Aaliyah doesn't believe in God. Maybe I can tell her that Jesus is the Son of God. And that I have even talked to God myself," she said.

At that moment, a bright light shone down from the sky. The Father was smiling.

"Now, My child, you can take your first step up toward heaven," He said.

18

And the Word [the Lord Jesus] became
flesh [a man] and dwelt among us.
                                    —John 1:14 KJV

3

Adam and Eve:

Our First Parents

"Here is how it all started," the Father God began speaking to Max and Vivi. "In the beginning of time, I created light, night, day, the stars, the seas, creatures to live in the seas, creatures to live on the dry land, and then a man—whom I named Adam. I did all of this in six days."

God formed man of the dust of the ground,
and breathed into his nostrils the breath of
life; and man became a living soul.
                                    —Genesis 2:7 KJV

The Father God continued, "I created Adam in My likeness. And on the seventh day, I rested for I was tired."

"I remember my mom telling me about Adam and Eve. Where was Eve when God made Adam?" asked Vivi. "And were they really our first parents?"

"I gave everything to Adam. He was the boss over all the fish, the birds, and the animals, but he became lonely for a friend who was like him. So I put him to sleep and removed one of his ribs, and with it I made the first woman."

"Ouch! That had to hurt Adam a lot," Max said.

"I made Eve to be Adam's helper, friend, and wife. The name *Adam* means 'many,' and *Eve* means 'the mother of all living,' and yes, they were your first parents. I put Adam and Eve in the Garden of Eden, and I gave them everything they could ever want. They were living in Paradise!

There was only one thing I asked of them. They could not eat from one of the trees—the tree called the Tree of the Knowledge of Good and Evil."

"Don't tell me they disobeyed You?" Vivi was horrified.

"Yes. I put Adam and Eve to a test, allowing Satan to roam around the Garden in the form of a snake. I knew that Satan would tempt Adam and Eve to disobey Me and eat from that tree.

"Unfortunately, the woman, Eve, was the first to fall for Satan's lies. He told her that if she ate the fruit from that tree, she would be just like Me—having My knowledge of good and evil."

"No, no, no! Why did Eve listen to the devil?" Max cried out.

The Father continued, "After Eve ate the fruit from the tree, she then turned to her husband, Adam, and convinced him to do the same thing.

"He did, but as soon as they ate the fruit, they were embarrassed and ashamed because they had no clothes on. Before they ate the fruit, they were both innocent, as pure as children. But when they disobeyed Me, they committed the first sin." The Father shook His head sadly.

"I had to punish Adam and Eve for disobeying Me. I sent them out of the Garden of Eden and made them work for food off the land they once had ruled over. If they had not disobeyed Me, they would have lived forever, but because they didn't listen, I pronounced a curse on them, on their relatives, and on the earth in general.

"Because of their sin, bad things now occur on the earth, and death comes to all people. Everyone grows old, and all people's bodies experience sickness, disease, and death.

"The lesson here is to never disobey Me. Life will be rough at times. But through My protection and guidance, you can make it through this world, and when you die, you will be with Me forever in heaven."

Vivi started crying. Max went over and put his paw around her neck.

"Why are you crying?" Max asked.

"Because Adam and Eve should not have disobeyed God. I promise I will never do that," Vivi said.

"Me, too," said Max.

"Very good, My child," the Father said to Vivi. "You may now take a second step toward heaven." Max and Viv took one step closer to Paradise.

In the beginning God created the heaven and the earth.
—Genesis 1:1 ESV

4

The Ten Commandments

As Max and Vivi climbed several steps, they were surrounded by the blue sky, puffy white clouds, and hundreds of colorful birds singing a melodious tune.

"Are we there yet?" Vivi asked Max. "Is this heaven?"

"This is the first heaven. God created three heavens, and this is the first," Max answered.

It was simply beautiful. The sky was clear, and the sun was shining. As the girl looked down, she could see what appeared to be the earth.

"We are up so high! Thank goodness I'm not afraid of heights," she said.

"Well, I am!" Max said gruffly, his body trembling.

"Don't worry, Max," said the booming voice from above. "I would never let anything happen to you. You are both doing a great job finding your way to heaven. Your next lesson is learning and obeying My rules."

"Rules? Like my mother's rules?" Vivi asked.

As God laughed, the clouds shook, and a brilliant light beamed down on them.

"Yes, like your mother's rules. But My rules are the most important to obey. If you want to get into heaven, you must obey them. My commandments are important, and children need to follow them to have a good and happy life.

"There are ten commandments. The first is: YOU SHALL HAVE NO OTHER GODS."

"What do you mean, Father? I can't love my dog, Max?" asked Vivi.

"Oh no! You can love your dog, your parents, and your friends, but your love for Me must always come first.

"The second commandment is this: YOU SHALL NOT HAVE OTHER GODS BEFORE ME. Don't put any other god before Me. Put Me first. Do not bow or worship statues, other people, or things."

"But there *is* only one God—it's You!" said Vivi.

"Yes, but some people worship statues and even other people and things before they worship Me," the Father answered.

"Well, Max and I know that You are the *only* God."

"The third commandment is: YOU SHALL NOT TAKE THE NAME OF THE LORD YOUR GOD IN VAIN. Never use My name in a disrespectful manner."

"Yes," Max spoke up. "How would you feel if someone said bad things and swore around your mom and dad? How do you think Jesus feels when someone says bad things about His Father?"

"Very good, Max. You are right," God answered. "Always respect My name and you will make Me very happy."

"The fourth commandment is: REMEMBER THE SABBATH DAY, the seventh day of the week. This means that Sunday is the Lord's Day. It represents the day I rested after I created the world and everything in it. This is the day you should set aside to rest and to worship Me."

"The fifth commandment is: HONOR YOUR FATHER AND YOUR MOTHER. Always respect your father and your mother. They are the parents I chose for you, and you must always love and obey them."

"The sixth commandment is: YOU SHALL NOT MURDER."

"MURDER!" Vivi exclaimed. "I can't even kill a bug!"

The heavenly Father laughed. "No, My child. I'm talking about taking another person's life. It is expressly forbidden, but as My Son, Jesus, taught during the Sermon on the Mount, the sin of murder begins in the heart. Even being angry with someone is not good. Learn to forgive and forget if someone does something to hurt you.

"The seventh commandment is: YOU SHALL NOT COMMIT ADULTERY. Although this doesn't affect you now, Vivi, when you grow up and get married, you must always respect and love your spouse. Marriage is the foundation of the family, which, in turn, stands as the foundation and most important building block of society.

"I created the family. I want a man and a woman to love each other, to get married, and to have children.

"The eighth commandment is: YOU SHALL NOT STEAL. No matter how many possessions you have, it all comes from Me. Everything you own is not really yours—it's Mine. I am just letting you borrow it.

"You should be thankful for what you have been given. You should not steal something because you want it and can't afford it. If you are tempted to steal something that belongs to someone else, pray for Me to give you strength and learn to be a great giver—not a taker.

"The ninth commandment is: DO NOT LIE. This is the commandment that most people have a hard time obeying. You may think, 'It's only a white lie or a fib,' but if you don't tell the truth, it's a lie. You might lie to avoid getting in trouble or to make yourself look better, but lying always will have bad results in the end.

"I am the God of truth. I love honesty, and I want you always to be honest.

"And the tenth and final commandment is: DO NOT COVET."

"What does 'covet' mean?" asked Vivi.

"To covet means to want things you can't or shouldn't have. This is another one of the devil's tricks. Satan always wants you to be dissatisfied—the opposite of how I want you to be. If you want something someone has or you are jealous of them, you are being selfish. I want you to be loving and giving—and grateful for what you have."

When the heavenly Father was done reciting the commandments, Vivi and Max sat with their mouths open.

"Wow! That's a lot to remember. I sure hope I always obey the commandments and make God happy," said Vivi.

"Me, too," said Max. "God created these laws, and they reflect His thinking. Disobeying the Ten Commandments shows a lack of love for God and other people."

"I'm sure you two have it in your hearts to do so. I am proud of you. Now, take another step up toward heaven," God the Father said.

In the beginning God created the
heavens and the earth.

—Genesis 1:1 NIV

5

Miracles

"Do you know what a miracle is?" God asked the dog and the young girl.

"I do," said Max. "My mom told me I was a miracle because I was the runt of the litter. I only weighed a few pounds, but I lived and grew up to be a big, healthy puppy."

"Yes, you are certainly a miracle, Max, but Jesus Christ performed many miracles in His lifetime on earth. He healed many people, and He even raised a man from the dead."

"I read that Jesus walked on water," said Vivi.

"No, that can't be! Nobody can walk on water," Max said.

"Well, My Son did, and He also fed four thousand men from seven loaves of bread and a few small fish," the Father told them as a pleased look crossed His face.

"Was He a magician? He had to be, because nobody can do those things unless they are a magician," Max said, puzzled.

"My Son was no magician. As it says in Acts 10:38, '*God anointed Jesus of Nazareth with the Holy Ghost and with power: who went about doing good, and healing all that were oppressed of the devil; for God was with him.*'

"Jesus is God. He is omnipotent—which means He is powerful. He is omnipresent, which means He is everywhere at once. He is omniscient, which means He is wise and knows everything."

"But how could He bring someone back from the dead? That's impossible," said Vivi.

"*Nothing* is impossible with Me. You must believe that all things are possible with Me—and with My Son, Jesus."

"Tell us about some of the other miracles Jesus did," Vivi said, excited.

"Yes…please tell us," Max agreed.

"Well, first of all, Jesus Himself is one of the greatest miracles, for He was conceived in Mary's body by the Holy Spirit. He is both God and human," God told them.

Max added, "Jesus healed blind people. He made people who were crippled to walk again. He calmed a raging storm, and He performed lots of other miracles to show us that God is real and loves us."

The Father smiled, and the entire sky was radiant.

"All the books in the world couldn't record all the miracles that Jesus Christ did. But I am constantly performing miracles every day in your life and your heart," He said.

"You are? How?" asked Vivi.

"Just the fact that you were born, you came into this world, and you are alive today is a *big* miracle. Your body itself is a miracle!" the Father told them.

"Even mine? I'm a dog!" asked Max.

"Yes, Max. All living things are miracles." God laughed as the clouds shook. "But the greatest miracle of all is when I call sinners to repentance and wash their sins away so they can spend eternity in heaven with Me! You see, I am still in the miracle business, and the Bible is a book of miracles. I work through people—from all walks of life—who believe in Me and allow Me to work through them."

"Well, Max and I believe in You," the girl said. "Maybe someday You will perform a miracle on me?"

"I'm sure I will," answered the Father. "Now take another step up."

For with God nothing shall be impossible.
—Luke 1:37 KJV

6

What it Will Be Like in Heaven

"Can't You tell us what it will be like when we go to heaven?" asked Vivi.

"Yes, I want to know what it will look like and what we will do there. Will the children have to go to school? Do they get to play with their friends—and their pets?" Max asked.

"Does it get cold? Will it snow there? Will people get sick?" Vivi anxiously asked.

"*Slow down*, My child." As the Father's heart warmed from all their questions, He smiled, and once again the sky was brilliant.

"First of all, there will be no more sickness and pain. Everyone will have a spiritual body. That doesn't mean you will be ghosts floating around, unable to interact with other things or with each other, but you will have a body like Jesus' resurrected body."

Vivi jumped up and down. "No more pain! Do You mean my cousin won't have cancer anymore?"

The Father answered, "There will be no more pain or disease.

"Revelation 21:4 says that I will wipe every tear from people's eyes. There will be no more death or mourning or crying or pain, for the old order of things has passed away. Heaven for My children will be a place of glorious life that never ends. There will be joy, peace, love, and beauty beyond description."

"Will we be able to recognize our loved ones?" Max asked.

"Of course, you will, Max. Your family and friends on earth will always be your family and friends—forever and ever!" the Father answered. "When My Son, Jesus, lived on earth, He talked a lot about eternity. He said that those who believed in Him would live forever in heaven.

"It is so beautiful in heaven. The wall that surrounds it is made of jasper, and the city itself is made from the purest gold. Even the street in the city is made of gold.

"And as far as the weather goes, there will be no more need for the sun or the moon. My glory will outshine the sun and the moon," the Father told them.

"Awesome! No more cold weather or snow and sleet!" Max exclaimed.

"What about our pets? Will we see them again?" Vivi asked the Father.

"God's creation story includes His creative work in the animal kingdom. Death is a natural and inevitable event for all living beings on the earth, but with your furry friends you have the hope and assurance that you will see them again in heaven."

"And how about our friends? How will we recognize them in heaven if they are dead?" Max asked.

God chuckled. "You will recognize them, although their appearance will change. The old will pass away in the twinkling of an eye.

"You can't even imagine what you will look like, for you will all have new bodies, like the body of My Son, Jesus. Just as Jesus looked like before He died, you will look like the person—and the dog—that you were."

After considering that thought for a few minutes, Vivi asked the Father, "What will we be doing in heaven? Won't it get boring if we are there forever?"

The Father reassured them. "First of all, you will worship Me in heaven. Second, you will eat with Me and My people, and third, you will live in complete peace and happiness with all of My other children—including the people in the Bible, like Abraham, Moses and David!

"You will be reunited with your parents, grandparents, children, grandchildren, friends, and loved ones from whom you have endured a painful separation when they died.

"You will have another chance to achieve the destiny you always wanted," said God. "You will have eternal life living among the angels, singing victory songs, and there will be no more evil or unhappiness."

"Heaven sure sounds like Paradise," said Max.

"It is, silly." Vivi laughed.

"Climb up another step, My child," God told Vivi.

As Max and Vivi took the next step, they noticed they were entering another realm. They were now in the second heaven.

44

"Let the earth bring forth living creatures according to their kinds—livestock and creeping things and beasts of the earth according to their kinds."
—Genesis 1:24 ESV

7

Jesus Died for Us

Vivi and Max were frightened, for they no longer were sitting among the puffy white clouds with birds flying around them.

They now were in a place they had once seen in a photo of outer space.

Sensing their fear, the Father said, "Do not be frightened. I am with you."

"Where are we?" asked Vivi.

"You are now in what I call mid-heaven, or the second heaven. Genesis 22:17 says that this is where Abraham's descendants would be as the 'stars of the heavens.' This is where the moon, the sun, the planets of the solar system, the distant stars and galaxies, and the rest of the universe is located.

"In the last and coming days, a war will be fought here. In this war, Satan will fall further down, and he can never enter the third heaven.

"Satan's realm will literally be on the earth for the final three and a half years, which is called the Great Tribulation," the Father told them.

"Please, God, protect us from Satan!" Vivi cried.

"Vivi, as a child of Mine, you will always be protected. That is why I sent My Son to die for your sins. I sent Jesus to teach people the truth about My kingdom and about everlasting life. Every person is a sinner, but Jesus came to earth to die in your place. Jesus was perfect. He did not die for His sins, for He had none. He died for your sins.

"His death in your place made it possible for you to enjoy everlasting life and receive My blessings. Jesus came to reveal Me, His Father, to you, for without Him you would not be able to see Me. Without Jesus, you would be forever fatherless, and by His coming to earth, all sin was done away with," the Father told them.

"But I remember reading how poor Jesus suffered for us." The girl began to sob.

Max walked over to her, put his paw in her lap, then licked her face. "I know. Jesus had to carry the cross that was so heavy because of people's sins. And I know that had to weigh a lot!" cried Max.

The Father explained, "Jesus carried the cross because He knew you and everyone else in the world was worth it. My Son had no sin, but He took on all the sins of the world. The nails that were driven into His hands and feet were really meant for you. The spear driven into His side was meant for you, and the crown of thorns on His head was meant to be your crown.

"How many people do you know who would go through all that for someone else? Well, Jesus did so that you could spend eternal life in heaven with Him."

"So, Jesus took all our sins so we could live with Him—and You—in heaven forever?" asked Vivi.

"Yes, My child. Jesus did all that for *you*!" answered the Father.

"I remember the time when my mom read that God sent His Son, Jesus, into the world to destroy the devil's work," Max said.

"The devil has tried over and over to destroy what Jesus did on the cross, but he cannot. And the devil's works that Jesus destroyed were deception (because Jesus is the Truth), death (because Jesus is the Resurrection and the Life), and sin (because Jesus is your Righteousness)," the Father said.

"I wish I could have carried that cross for Jesus," cried Vivi.

"Me too. I know I'm just a dog, but maybe I could have helped by pulling it with my teeth," said Max.

The sky lit up like a Christmas tree as God smiled.

"You two have made Me very proud. Now, come a step closer to Me."

"For God did not send his Son into the world to condemn the world, but to save the world through him."

—John 3:17 NIV

8

The Promises of God

As Vivian and Max climbed several steps, they were caught between the second and the third heaven.

The sky was so bright they had to blink several times to adjust their eyes. Hundreds of cherubim, seraphim, and archangels were flying around, singing, and playing harps.

On one side of the stairway were several people who seemed to be stuck in place—unable to move up or down.

Vivian immediately recognized one woman. It was her aunt Betty, who had died years earlier in a car wreck.

The girl loved her aunt very much and was excited to see her.

"Aunt Betty! It's me...Vivi! What are you doing here? Why are you standing on the side? Why aren't you up in heaven?" the girl called out.

Instead of her aunt answering her, the Father spoke.

"Your aunt is not here with Me yet because she has not accepted Jesus as her Savior," He said.

"Oh no! Aunt Betty! You *must* accept Jesus as your Savior. If you don't, you'll never get into heaven, and I'm going there now with my dog, Max."

But before her aunt could answer, Vivi and Max were brought even closer to God.

Sad that her aunt seemed to be frozen in place, Vivi began to cry. As tears fell from her little face, they dropped down to earth.

"Do not be sad, My child. I promise you that your aunt will be there when you come to live with Me," the Father said.

"You PROMISE? I know sometimes people make promises they can't keep. My friends always make promises and break them!" Vivi said.

"Well, I always keep My promises. And I make many promises to My children," the Father replied.

"What are Your promises?" Max asked, jumping up and down.

"Well, you had better sit down, because this is going to be a very long lesson," the Father said with a smile.

"My holy Book is called the Bible. It is filled with many of My promises. From the beginning of the Book in Genesis to the end of the Book in Revelation, it tells that ordinary people—like you, Vivi—have received My promises. I promised to bless Abraham, and I did (Genesis 12:2–3). I promised that those who believe in Jesus and accept My forgiveness of their sins would be saved (Mark 16:16)—"

Viv interrupted the Father. "But how can *we* count on Your promises to us? We are just a little girl and her dog…"

"My sweet child, you must have total trust and faith in Me," He answered. "Remember, I am not a man. I don't have a fallen nature, for I have never sinned or lied. You can count on My promises because I am unchanging. Unlike other people, I never change. I am always the same.

"I was, I am, and I always will be. I will give you wisdom if you ask. Just ask Me, and I will answer—I promise," the Father said. "The devil will flee from you if you resist him. Satan will always try to take you from Me, for he is a liar! So, when he tempts you…resist! Submit to Me, your Father, and give Me your life. As you follow Me, you can be assured that Satan will try to take you away from Me," God said.

Max yelped in fear. "The devil! Please, God, promise to keep him away from me and Vivi."

The Father reassured the dog. "Max, I promise. And one last promise from Me is that whoever believes in My Son, Jesus Christ, and is baptized will be saved."

"Baptized? I already was baptized when I was a baby," said Vivi.

"Well, you must be baptized and born again in order to enter the kingdom of heaven with Me," God said.

Just then a shower of water fell on Vivi and Max's heads. Max shook his wet body, and Vivi wiped the water from her eyes.

"You are now baptized in the name of the Father, the Son, and the Holy Spirit," the Father said.

"Amen!" Vivi and Max said in unison.

Jesus replied, "I tell you the truth, unless you are born again, you cannot see the Kingdom of God."
—John 3:3 NLT

9

Born Again

Vivi wasn't sure why she felt so different, but she had never felt so calm and peaceful as when the water poured onto her head. She didn't actually see the heavenly Father pouring the water, but she knew He had.

At that moment, thousands of angels began singing, and the sky flashed with bright colors as if it were the Fourth of July!

Max agreed that he felt the same way, too. He had always been a nervous dog, and Vivi had always worried about everything. It was just her nature, for her father was the same way. Max and Vivi would worry about things they had no control over, and most of the time they worried about things that never even happened.

As the Father saw how happy the girl and her dog were, He smiled. Again, when He did, the sky lit up as the angels sang songs of praise in harmony.

The people in heaven all gathered around God, bowing before Him. At that moment, Vivi and Max caught a glimpse of what God looked like. Although it wasn't perfectly clear, they had never seen anything so beautiful!

Heaven was exactly what they had imagined it would look like. There were beautiful flowers in every color and shape. Their aroma was as sweet as nectar.

There was one flower in particular they had never seen on the earth. It was a pink, heart-shaped flower.

"Thank You, God! I feel so peaceful. Now that we are baptized, can we take the final step into heaven?" Vivi anxiously asked.

"Yes, me too. I want to live with You, Father," Max said. "It is *so* beautiful here, and everything is perfect."

"No, I'm afraid it is not yet time for the two of you to live here," the Father said.

Tears began to run down the girl's face. As they dropped from her cheeks, an angel caught them.

"But why? We were good students, weren't we?" Max asked.

"You were the *best*!" the Father said. "But you must go back home and tell your parents and friends everything I have taught you. It's very important, for the world is in bad shape and it breaks My heart.

"The two of you will be My disciples, teaching those who do not believe in Me that I am God and that I love each and every one of them the same.

"You must tell them about Adam and Eve and the first sin. You must tell them that Jesus is My Son.

"Tell them all the miracles Jesus did while He was on the earth and how He suffered and died on the cross so they could live forever with Him in Paradise.

"Don't forget to tell them about My promises and how I keep them, and most of all, tell them they *must* accept Jesus as their Savior and be baptized," the Father said.

"But we don't want to leave You! We want to stay here," said Vivi.

"You must go! But I promise, you will be back here when your work is done on earth. And you *know* I keep My promises." The Father smiled. "I will always be with you, protecting you. And I will send a sign now and then to show you that I'm there."

Just then, Vivi and Max felt a warm sensation that seemed to go right through them.

The next minute, they were standing back in the park, but there was no stairway to heaven in front of them anymore.

"Was that a dream, Vivi?" Max asked.

"I don't know, but if it was, I wish it had never ended," the girl said.

They walked back home quietly. As they entered the house, Vivi's mom ran over to her daughter.

"Where have you two been? I've been worried sick!" her mother said.

"We've been to heaven, Mom. We were talking with our heavenly Father," the girl said.

"You really have some imagination, child!" Her mother laughed. "And what a strange-looking flower in your hair! Where did you get that?"

Just then, a double rainbow appeared in the sky.

Vivi and Max smiled as they looked up at heaven, for they knew this was a sign from God.

THE END
(But it's really only the beginning!)

Epilogue

While writing this book, I learned so much. I thought I knew a lot about our heavenly Father and His Son, Jesus Christ, but looking through a child's eye, I saw them in a different way.

Children are innocent and born pure. They are not tainted until the world and its evil ways get ahold of them.

How much better would the world be if children grew up with nothing but love and kindness?

If there were no more judging, criticizing, or abuse—that would be a perfect world—as God created it to be.

I hope the teachings in this book have enlightened you. I pray we can join together as one in the battle of the heart.

Children are the future, and if they are taught about Jesus and what He did for us, perhaps we can help change the world back the way God wanted it to be. All that matters is getting people to the finish line of their lives so they can spend eternity in heaven with the Lord.

God has been so faithful to us, and I am sure that the next world is more real and better than this one.

Other Books by Victoria M. Howard

Gunner: An Enchanting Tale of a Racehorse

MAX, THE BOLOGNESE DOG SERIES
Max Goes to School
The Adventures of Max and Molly
Max Saves the World

Junior: The Racehorse That Won the Kentucky Derby

Junior and Elena: A (Horse) Love Story

Whispers from God: 365 Daily Devotionals

Kentucky Horse Park: Paradise Found

The Real Vivian Grace and Max

About the Author

Victoria M. Howard is an author, a horse breeder, and an ordained Christian minister. She has written dozens of books in the areas of fiction, nonfiction, children's books, and spiritual life.

At one time, Ms. Howard represented her state in the Mrs. USA pageant, where she finished third and won "Most Photogenic."

In 2000, Victoria spent several days living with an aboriginal tribe in Australia, observing their culture and way of life and listening to their "Dreamland" stories.

Today, Victoria resides in Florida with her dog, Max, and her horses. She enjoys spending time with her granddaughter, Vivian Grace.

CPSIA information can be obtained
at www.ICGtesting.com
Printed in the USA
BVHW011219110422
633959BV00010B/384

9 781685 562526